HOW TO DRAW
FOR THE ARTISTICALLY ANXIOUS

JOHN BIGWOOD

LOM
ART

ILLUSTRATED BY JOHN BIGWOOD
EDITED BY JOCELYN NORBURY
AND PHILIPPA WINGATE

DESIGNED BY JOHN BIGWOOD
COVER DESIGN BY ZOE BRADLEY

First published in Great Britain in 2018 by LOM ART, an imprint of
Michael O'Mara Books Limited, 9 Lion Yard, Tremadoc Road, London SW4 7NQ

W www.mombooks.com
f Michael O'Mara Books
🐦 @OMaraBooks

A CIP catalogue record for this book is available from the British Library.

ISBN: 978-1-910552-76-6

2 4 6 8 10 9 7 5 3 1

Printed in China.

INTRODUCTION

Do you find people impossible to draw? Are you intimidated by facial expressions and complicated poses? Don't put down your pens just yet – a solution lies within these pages.

Forty-six watercolour splodges are waiting to be transformed into a cast of cool and quirky characters. All you have to do is use the illustrated examples as inspiration to add faces, poses, and accessories. Worry not about wonky lines, weird features, smudges or scribbles – every stroke of your pen adds personality and flair. These characters are yours to bring to life.

Add a pout to a pin up, adorn a rapper with his rightful bling, and give a boy-band all the right moves, as you forget your fears and reveal your inner artist. What are you waiting for? Just pick up a pen and follow the prompts to create a host of characters that celebrate the perfectly imperfect in all of us!

DOG WALKER

Strolling along

Freedom!

Poo bag

Careless whistle

Dog on the loose

Lead

Windswept scarf

Legs

Chasing dog

Casual stroll

Sprinting dog

Strutting dog

ARTIST

Art critic

Artistic genius

Con artist

Smock

Neckerchief

Legs

Work of art

Paintbrush

Palette

Easel

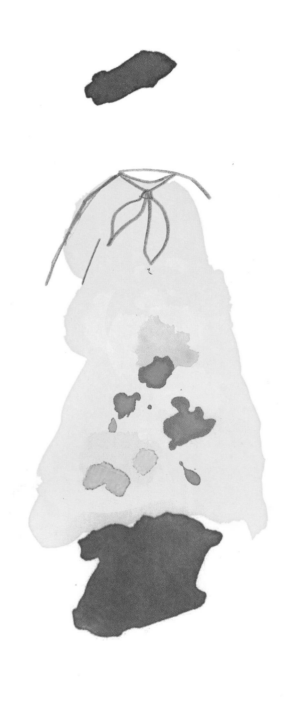

PiN UP

Some like it hot

Legs

Happy Birthday, Mr. President

Face

Pout

Singing

Birthday arms

Body

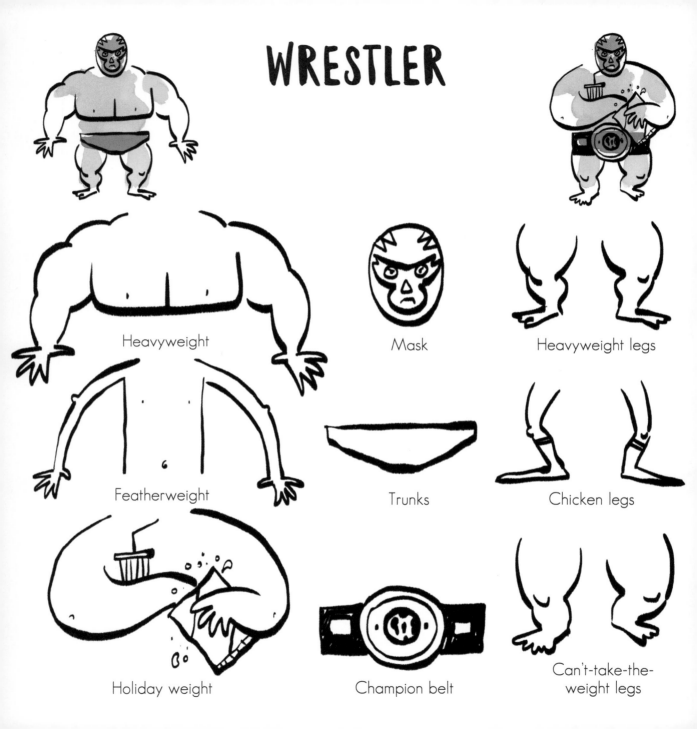

WRESTLER

Heavyweight

Mask

Heavyweight legs

Featherweight

Trunks

Chicken legs

Holiday weight

Champion belt

Can't-take-the-weight legs

I'M WITH THE BAND

John

Ringo

Paul

George

Wrong band

French horn

Yellow suit

Pink suit

Blue suit

Red suit

Doesn't suit

Trumpet

Drum

Clarinet

FiSHERMAN

Gone fishing

Weather beaten

Stow-away

"It was THIS big"

Wellies

Fishing rod

Designer wellies

Waterproof

Hearty pipe

Woah! That's
a big one!

Big
disappointment

CLOWN

Funny clown

Scary clown

Tears of a clown

Do-you-want-fries-with-that clown

IN BUSINESS

Black Thursday

Dressed to impress

Dress-down Friday

Business folder

Economic boom

Takeaway salad

Credit crunch

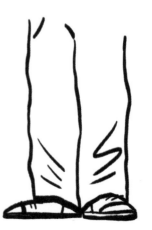

Briefcase

PUNK

Rebellion

Anarchy

Minor revolution

Serious hardware

Leopard

Let it grow

Profile

STUDENT

Top marks

Bottom of the class

Egg head

Bed head

Scroll

#graduation

Graduation / Dressing gown

Homeward bound

Library fine

SUPERHERO

Face

Mask

Hair

Glasses

Hail the taxi

Hail, the hero

Cape

Incognito

Taking flight

ELVIS
IMPERSONATOR

All shook up

Peanut butter and banana face

Day-off Elvis

Stage Elvis

Dressing-room Elvis

FARMER

At one with nature

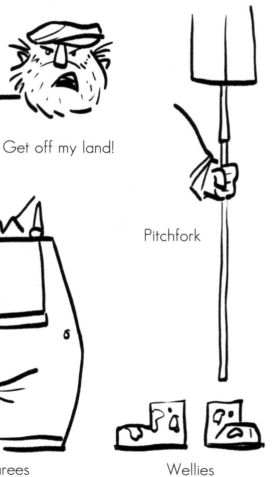

Get off my land!

Pitchfork

Pet pig

Dungarees

Wellies

Attack pig

BEAUTY SCHOOL DROPOUT

Shampoo and set

What's love got to do with it?

Emergency wig

Eyes

Nose

Coy smile

Beauty spot

Face and neck

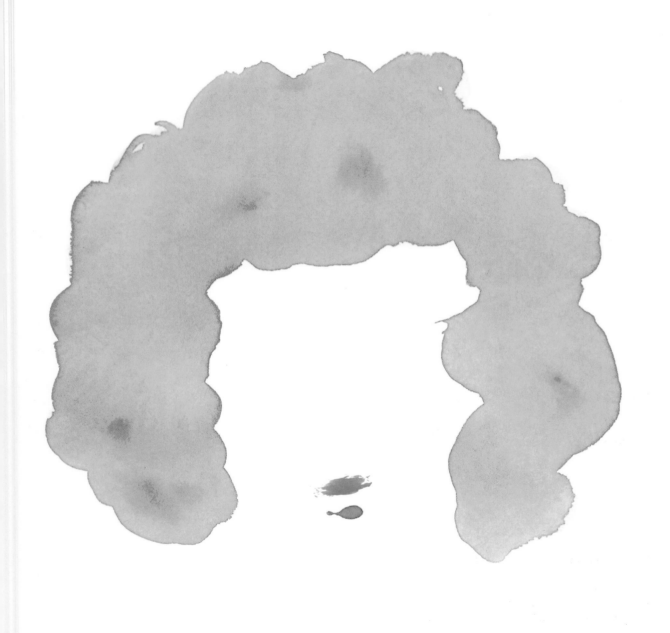

DETECTIVE

Thoughtful

Suspicious

Confounded

Private eye

Off-duty

Legs

Armed and dangerous

Coat

Bloodhound

Bling hound

Magnifying glass

Pipe

RAPPER

No downloads

Top of the pops

Billboard hit

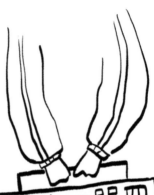

Serious beats

Tracksuit bottoms

Fresh threads

'Sup G

Straight outta the '80s

Pristine snapback

Headphones

Chillin'

DEEP SEA DIVER

Ah, pretty fishes

Pretty fishy

Shark attack!

Feeling seasick

Diving helmet

Definitely seasick

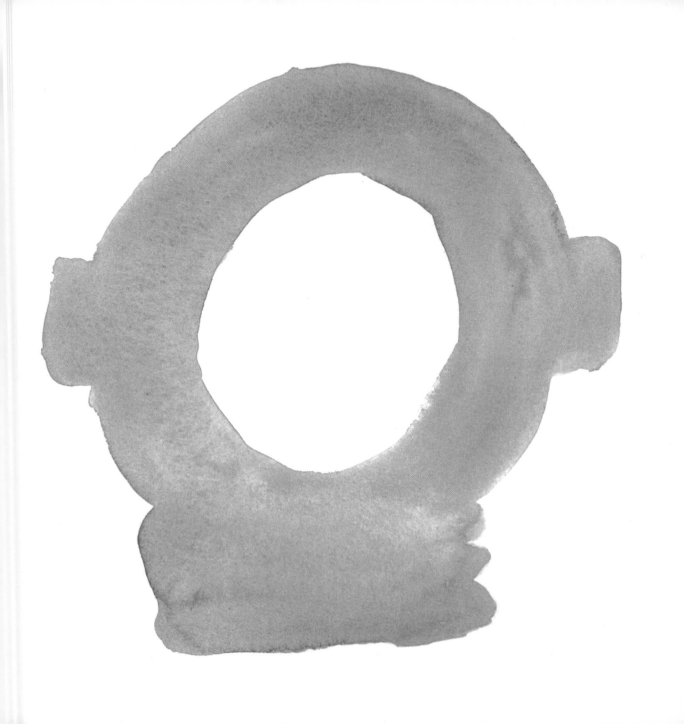

COUPLES

Old flames

Young love

Walking stick

Mobile phone

Newspaper

News feed

Hot chocolate

Flat white

EXERCISE
ENTHUSIAST

Deep burn

Burning calories

Burning the candle
at both ends

Shorts

Muscle vest

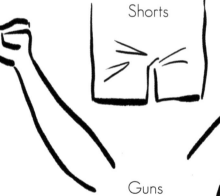

Guns

Legs of steel

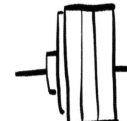

Weights

MASTER OF DISGUISE

Grandpa

Geek

Fancy

Blind as a bat

Nose

Hair

Tom Selleck 'tache

Mouth

Goatee

ELF

Santa's elf

Sulky elf

Satan's elf

Bauble

Bell

Fur trim

 Ears

AUDREY

Gloved hand

Bow lips

Breakfast at Tiffany's

Breakfast in bed

Breakfast the morning
after the night before

Face and neck

Cat eyes

Panda eyes

Do not disturb

BARiSTA

Single espresso

Double hazelnut latte

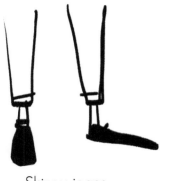
Soy latte, extra hot, whipped cream

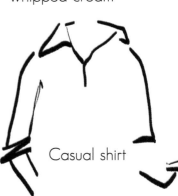
Casual shirt

Skinny jeans

Frothy coffee

Espresso

Take away

Skinny legs

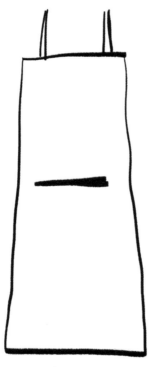
Apron

Avocado on toast

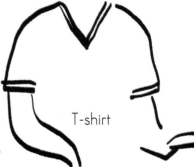
T-shirt

DANCER

Prima ballerina
assoluta

Tutu

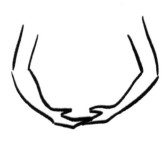

Poised

Caffeine hit

First position

Second position

Third position

And ... relax

SELFiE

Photo ready

Photo NOT ready

Filtered face

Photobomb

The wrong cheeks

BOY BAND

The joker

The one with
all the moves

The
talented one

The dreamy one

The bad boy

Guitar

Mic

Triangle

Cow bell

FLAMENCO DANCER

Olé

Oh no!

Fan

Castanets

Roses

Ruffles

Hair flower

PARK AVENUE PRINCESS

Uptown

Downtown

Get outta town

Scrunchie

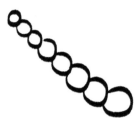

Pearls

Family jewels

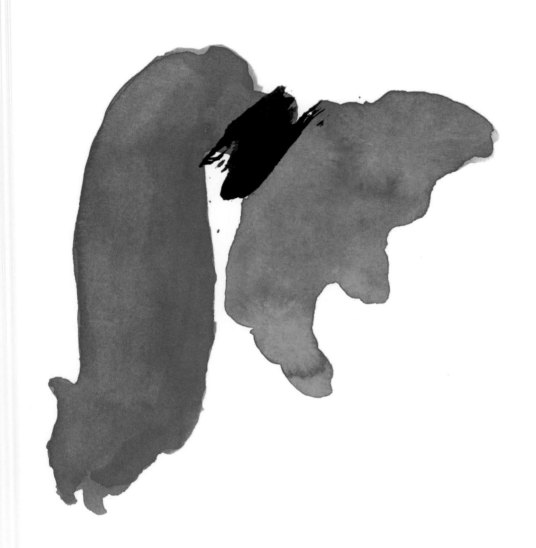

WINDOW CLEANER

Cor blimey guv'nor!

Stairway to heaven

Snakes and ladders

Soap suds

Squeegee

Window frame

Bird poo

Soapy cloth

SYNCHRONIZED SWIMMERS

High score

Nul points

Swimming cap

Nose clip

Water ripples

Swimsuit

Perfect points

Cramp!

NUTTY PROFESSOR

Back to the future

Back to the drawing board

Back to bed

Wild hair

Anyone seen my goggles?

MERMAID

Singing siren

Salt water plays havoc

Fish tail

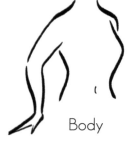

Body

Seashell bikini

Snail-shell bikini

Fairy tail

Sea rock

HiPSTER

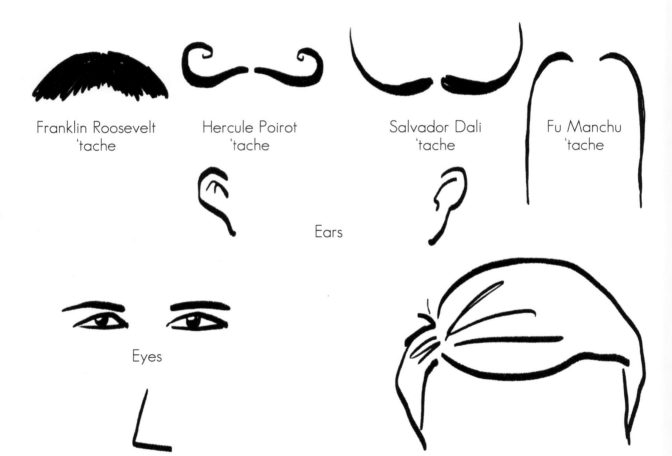

Franklin Roosevelt
'tache

Hercule Poirot
'tache

Salvador Dali
'tache

Fu Manchu
'tache

Ears

Eyes

Nose

Hair

HiGH ROLLER

Fan of money

Fan of cards

Gambling chips

Sunglasses

Tie

Casino Royale

Poker face

Losing hand

Ka-ching!

BEARDY

Trend-setter

Carefully coiffed

Specs appeal

Insecure

Carefully concealed bald spot

Going underground

CHEF

Head chef

Sous chef

Little Chef

Dishwasher

Apron

Tunic

Legs

Sweary

Slice and dice

Scrubber

BiRD LADY

Feed the birds

Aargh, incoming!

Pretty birdies

Dinner is served

Attack pigeon

Boots

Coat

SPLAT!

ROCK CHICK

On fleek

Well groomed

Natural

Well natural

Microphone

On-trend crop

Microphone

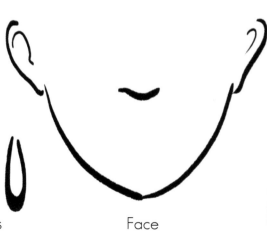

Mouth

Hoop earrings

Face

ORCHESTRA CONDUCTOR

Lost in music

Lost the mojo

Lost the baton

Sound of music

Coat

Legs

Hair

Music stand

PROM QUEEN

Princess hair

Overdone it

Undateable

The friend zone

Perfect date

Arms

Dream dress

Blisters

BRIDE AND GROOM

Wedding hair

Bride of Frankenstein

Well groom-ed

Not groom-ed

Something old

Something new

Something borrowed

AGEING FACE

Baby face

Teen angst

Midlife crisis

The golden years

LiON TAMER

Not a performing seal

Will jump for treats

Failed it

Nailed it

Hoop

King of the jungle

Queen of the ring

NEWS FLASH

Bad news

Good news

News to me

Power suit

Script

Meaningless graphic

GLAMOUR GiRL

Wide-eyed and innocent

 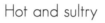

Hot and sultry

Too much eyelash glue

Face

Va-va-voom hair

Nose

Lips

BEAUTY SLEEP

Night light

Night-time reading

Night cap

Night cap

Night dress

Starry, starry night

Beauty sleep

Slippers

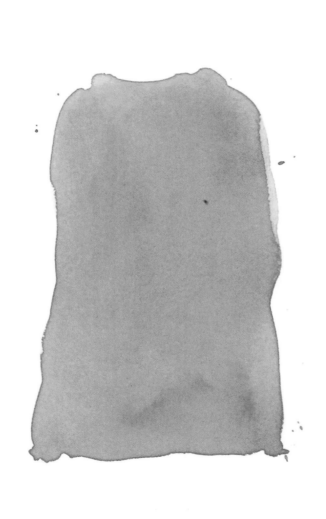

Minnow, go to sleep and dream,
Close your great big eyes;
Round your bed Events prepare
The pleasantest surprise ...

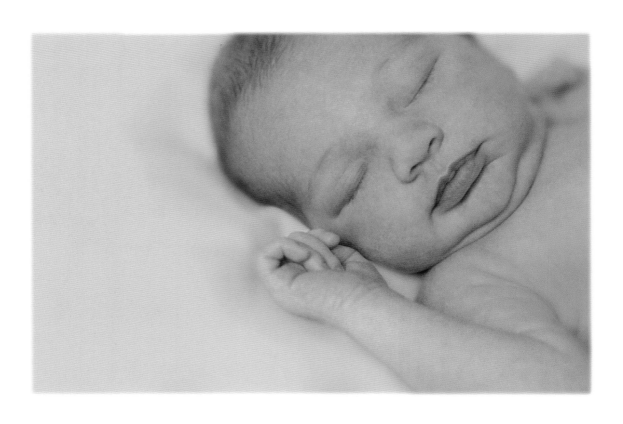

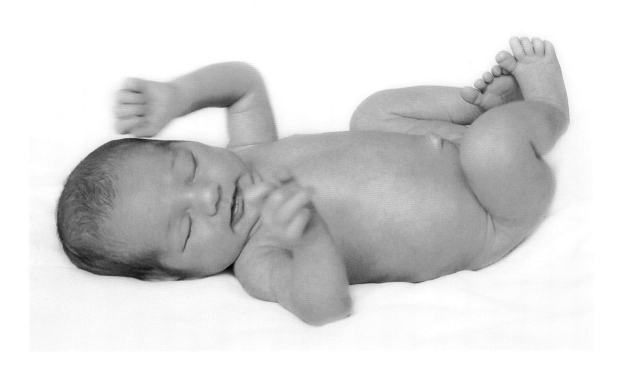

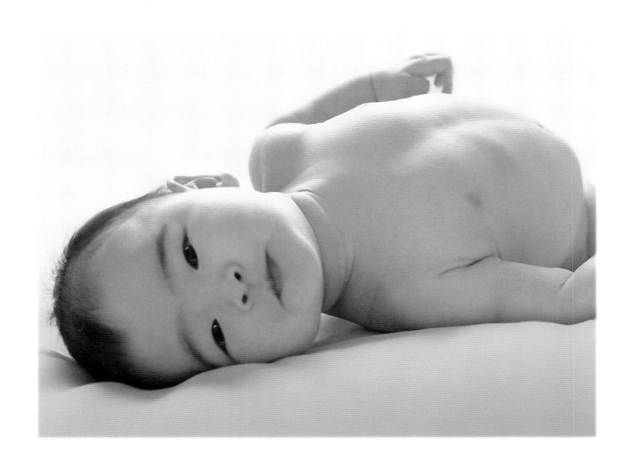

Sweet moans, dovelike sighs,

Chase not slumber from thy eyes!

Sweet moans, sweeter smiles,

All the dovelike moans beguiles.

Sleep, sleep, happy child!

All creation slept and smil'd

A Cradle Song

WILLIAM BLAKE

'I have no name;
I am but two days old.'
What shall I call thee?
'I happy am,
Joy is my name.'
Sweet joy befall thee!

Pretty joy!
Sweet joy, but two days old.
Sweet joy I call thee:
Thou dost smile,
I sing the while;
Sweet joy befall thee!

Infant Joy

WILLIAM BLAKE

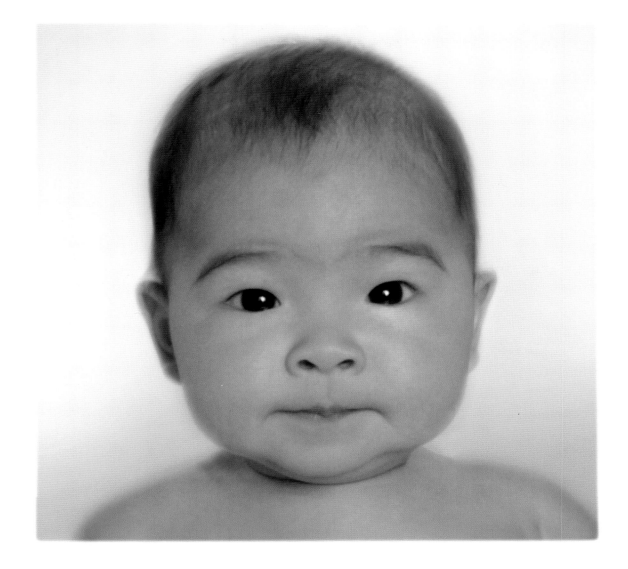

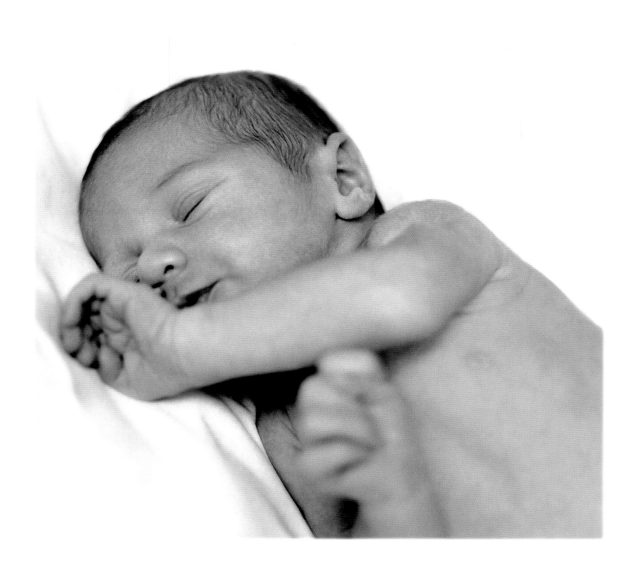

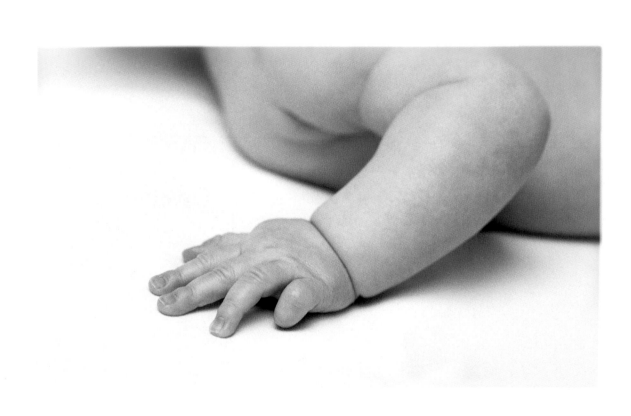

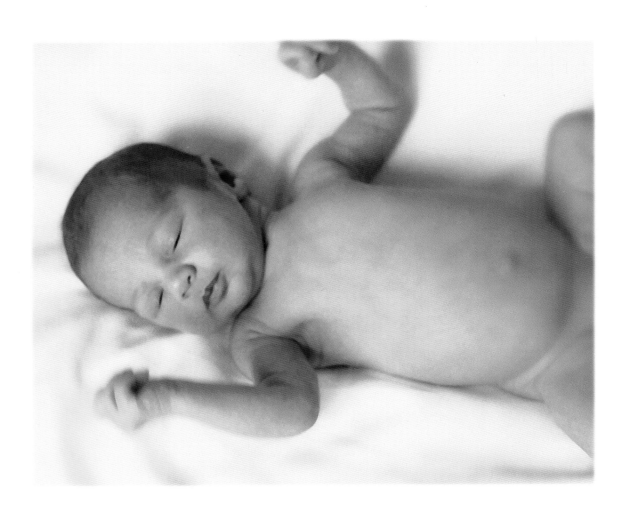

Do you see that kitten chasing so prettily her own tail? If you could look with her eyes, you might see her surrounded with hundreds of figures performing complex dramas, with tragic and comic issues, long conversations, many characters, many ups and downs of fate, —and meantime it is only puss and her tail.

Experience

RALPH WALDO EMERSON

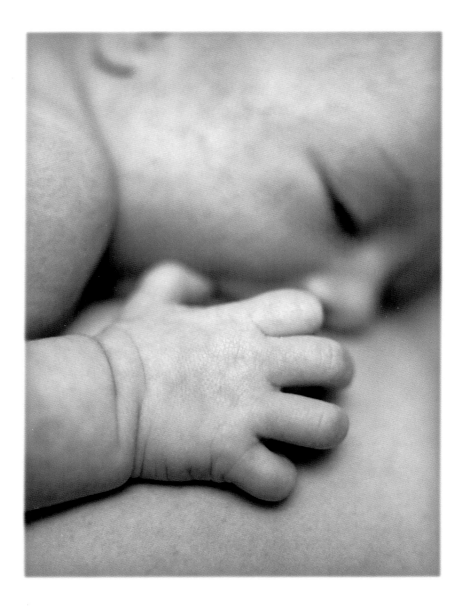

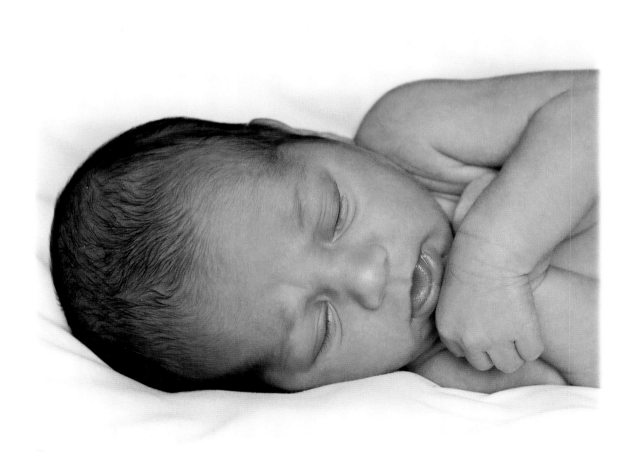

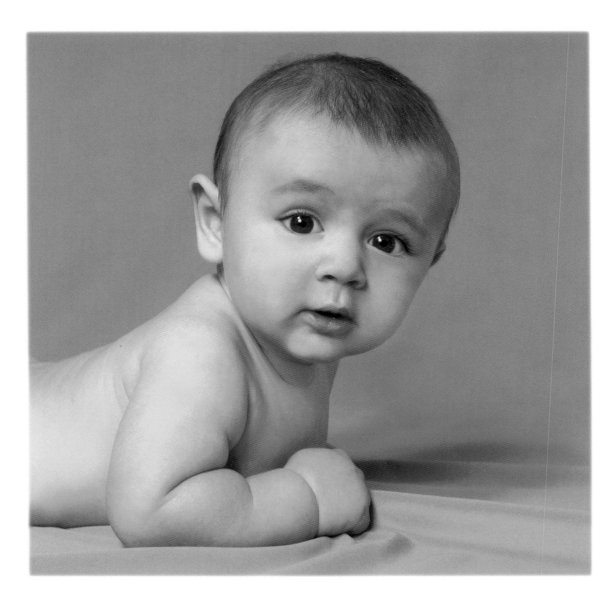

I sigh that kiss you,
For I must own
That I shall miss you
When you have grown.

A Cradle Song

WILLIAM BUTLER YEATS

What feeling is so nice as a child's hand in yours? So small, so soft and warm, like a kitten huddling in the shelter of your clasp.

Calendar of
Love and
Inspiration

MARJORIE HOLMES

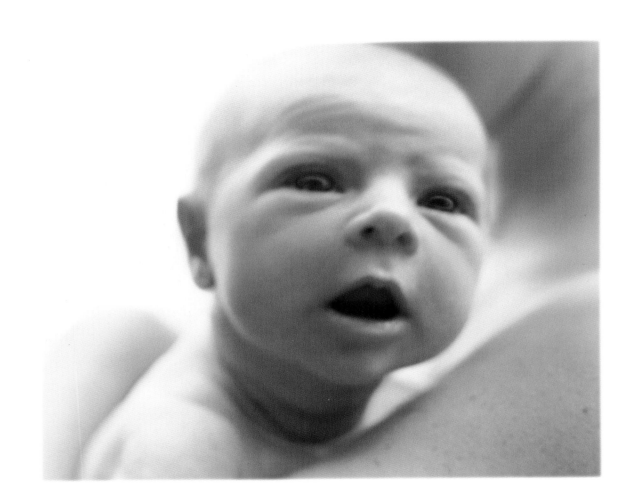

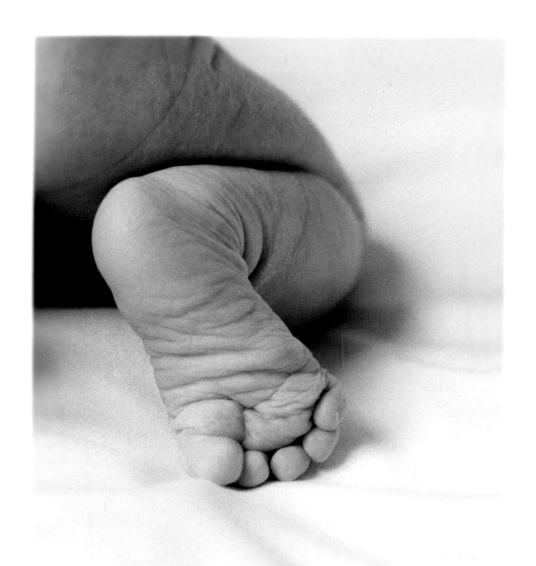

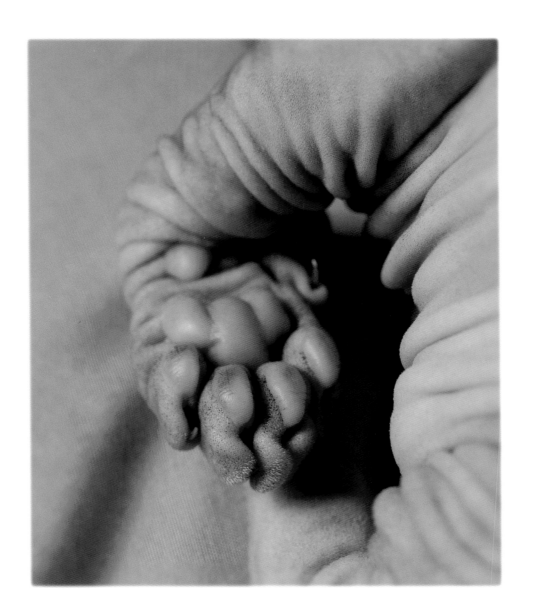

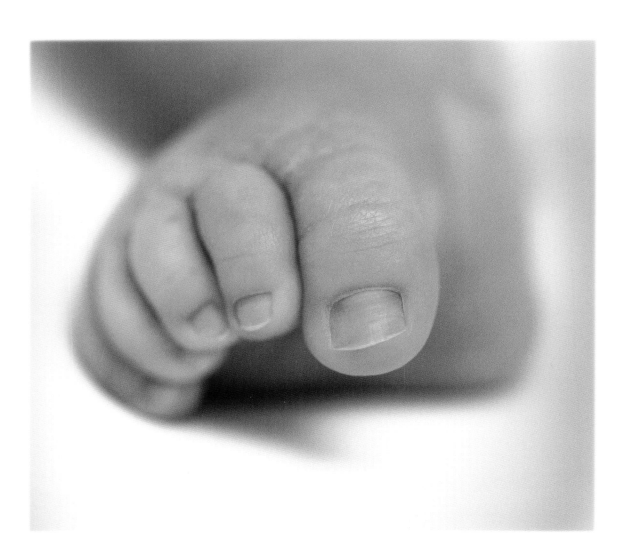

Now and then I may possess
Hours of perfect gladsomeness.
—Pleased by any random toy;
By a kitten's busy joy,
Or an infant's laughing eye

The Kitten
and Falling Leaves

WILLIAM WORDSWORTH

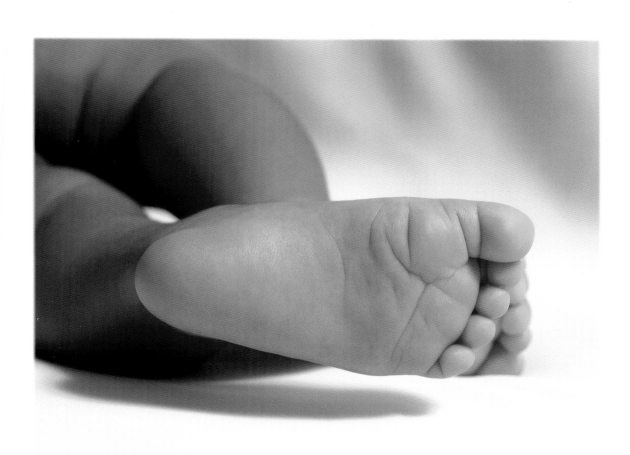

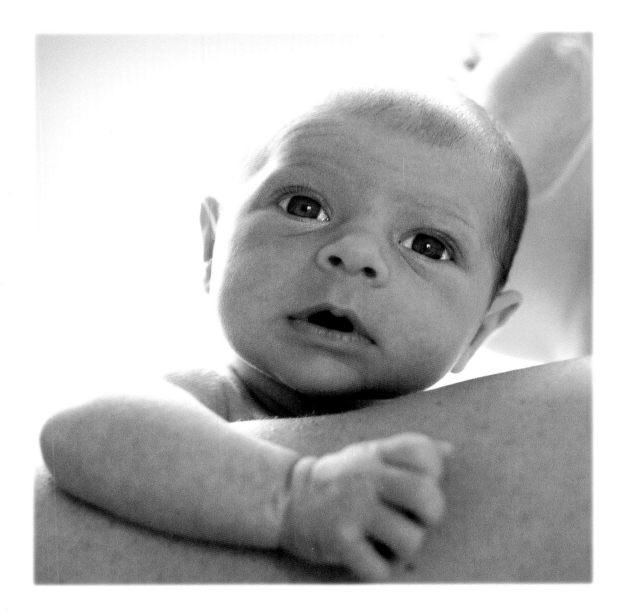

my little one

VICKY CEELEN

Stewart, Tabori & Chang
New York

To my children, Vincent and Rafäel,
and to Kelly who posed for this book.